PUZZLE PANIC

BY DONNA LUGG PAPE AND JEANETTE GROTE
ILLUSTRATED BY TOM EATON

SCHOLASTIC BOOK SERVICES
NEW YORK · TORONTO · LONDON · AUCKLAND · SYDNEY · TOKYO

ISBN: 0-590-10314-8

12 11 10 9 8 7   9/7 0 1/8

Printed in the U.S.A.

Space Maze

Grokko 1839 ZX will be earthbound forever unless he can get through the Finks Museum and out the back to where the Grok ship is hovering. Grokko needs YOU!

FINKS MUSEUM

Magic How To

How do you get a horse for hire?

Put four bricks under it.

How do you make a bandstand?

Pull their chairs away.

How can you change a pumpkin into another vegetable?

Throw it up into the air and it will come down squash.

Name It

The words below are really scrambled names for the objects. When you've labeled them, try making sentences using all the new words. (Just add connective words like a, the, on, and, he.)

1. TOP
2. MANE
3. PORE
4. SALE
5. RATS

6. BLEAT
7. GRIN
8. HOSE
9. WAS
10. FLEA

saw   star   leaf   ring

pot   sope   shoe

DAN   seal   WILL

Word Bargain

In this puzzle you get two for one—that is, two uses for the same word in each sentence. Example: When I wear *blue,* I feel *blue.*

1. Dump the coffee _____ anywhere on the _____.

2. Some dogs will _____ even at the _____ of a tree.

3. Cars and rhinos both have _____.

4. Debby's _____ were fixed on the _____ of the potatoes.

5. Don't play _____ in the _____ room (dance hall).

6. He set the _____ of the clock with his _____.

7. When the ship's bells _____, put the _____ on your finger.

8. She was wearing a _____ when she made that _____ of the tongue.

9. Don't _____ in the bus station when you buy your round- _____ ticket.

10. The _____ will _____ out the window when you open it.

Color Clues

Fill in the colors, using the clues, and you'll see what the pot of gold is at the end of.

1. Color of most fire engines.
2. Name of a fragrance; also a light tint of purple.
3. Color of some lemonade and a panther in the movies.
4. The color of leaves in spring and summer.
5. The color of the clear sky.
6. Round Florida fruit.
7. Color of lemons.

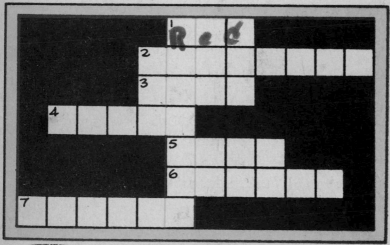

Dates 'n' Stuff

Across:

1. Year Columbus discovered America.
5. Year of science fiction TV show.
6. Days in a week.
7. Christmas Day.
9. Months in five years.
11. Four weeks (in days).
13. Hours in a day.
15. Days in a year.
18. A century.
20. Zero
21. Date the Pilgrims first landed at Plymouth.
23. 1620-1920.
24. "_____Up."

Down:

1. Bicentennial year.
2. Year of California Gold Rush, 18____.
3. Last two numbers of year before 1900.
4. A pair.
5. New Year's Day.
7. Twins.
8. Weeks in a year.
10. Two cents written after $1.
12. Half past eight.
14. Independence Day.
16. _____ Million Dollar Man.
17. States in the U.S.A.
18. Months in a year.
19. Double O Seven.
21. A decade.
22. Five dozen.
23. Trio.

This is not a crossword but a cross-*numbers* puzzle.
(Any cross numbers in your class?)

Alphabet Soup

Use any letter from the alphabet that gives these sentences some sense.

_____ am going to be late today.

The blue _____ is a bird.

_____ marks the spot.

Are _____ ready for the big surprise?

A _____ is a vegetable.

I _____ the _____ (stinging insect).

_____ you going to get a camera for Christmas?

The actor took his _____ from the prompter.

Will you _____ near the _____ (ocean)?

My mother likes to drink _____ .

_____ whiz, how can I do all that in an hour?

_____ boy, that bike is just the one I wanted.

_____ don't we have a party?

This store has everything from A to _____ .

She likes a round neck, but I like a _____ .

State Scramble

After you cross out every square in which the answer is 8, unscramble the letters in the squares that are left, to find the name of a state in the U.S.A.

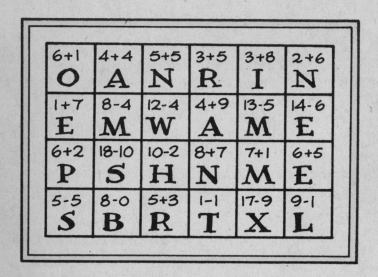

6+1	4+4	5+5	3+5	3+8	2+6
O	A	N	R	I	N
1+7	8-4	12-4	4+9	13-5	14-6
E	M	W	A	M	E
6+2	18-10	10-2	8+7	7+1	6+5
P	S	H	N	M	E
5-5	8-0	5+3	1-1	17-9	9-1
S	B	R	T	X	L

WHAT STATE DO YOU LIVE IN?

A STATE OF **CONFUSION!**

CALISOTA

MINNEZONA

ALAKOTA

Bee-lieve

Why are bees like kisses?

> *Bee-cause they're found on two lips (tulips).*

Why do bumblebees hum?

> *Bee-cause they don't know the words.*

What is a bee in the fall?

> *Bee-lated.*

What is a bee on a flower?

> *Bee-lighted.*

Paint-A-Color

There's a color hidden in each of these words. As you find it, add it to the _____ . (Circled letters will give you this word.)

Across:
2. Bread
4. Plumper
5. General
6. Whistle

Down:
1. Mellowly
3. Bulletin
4. Pumpkins
7. Stand

Twist Around

Start with the marked D. Moving clockwise around the circle, underline the 3rd letter after that D. Keep circling and underlining every 3rd letter until you have a sentence. How many times can you say it fast before you trip over those darn D's?

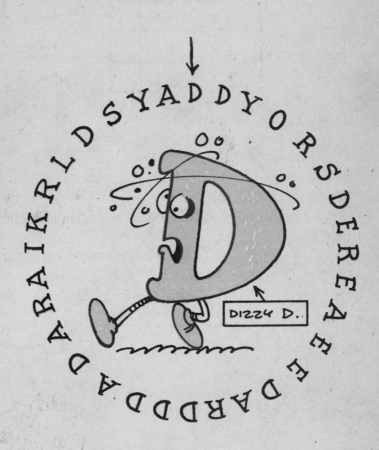

Magic Square

Fill in the words so that the square reads the same across and down.

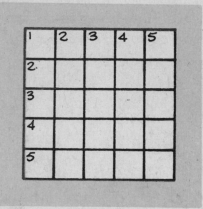

1. Halloween creature wearing a sheet.
2. To break out of an egg.
3. Furry, web-footed swimming animal.
4. The setting of a crime.
5. A magic number: wishes, blind mice, musketeers, and kings.

Hidden Saying Rebus

There's a wise old saying hidden in this rebus. Can you find it? Write down the letters of the words for the pictures and add or subtract letters as shown.

Farm Charm Crossword

Across:

2. Rail Road (abbrev.) stops where farmers take their crops.
3. A bull, wherever he goes, wears a _____ in his nose.
5. He grows the food we eat — broccoli or meat.
6. It's a _____ of hay to make a horse's day.
7. You get milk from a _____ . (It rhymes with Mary.)
10. Knocked Out (abbrev.) is what Farmer Stout is.
11. Peas grow in a _____ . (It rhymes with sod.)
13. Farm dogs howl and sometimes _____ .

Down:

1. It will appear in many an ear.
2. It's filled to the brim around the _____ .
3. Same as 2 across.
4. Where seeds are sown and grown.
5. A tool for pitching hay, and eating, every day.
8. Creatures all, great and small.
9. It's made from milk and a health food too:
   It's spelled with an O, a G, and a U.
12. This barn _____ flies at night.
   He's supposed to be quite bright.

Hidden Creature Feature

Underline the letters that spell a bird or animal hidden in each sentence below. Then fit them into the boxes opposite. One creature is given to start you off. You don't have to do them in order. As you fill in the puzzle the letters will give you clues.

1. Abraham Lincoln became famous, even though he was a poor boy.
2. If you do good work, you get good grades.
3. How long does the puzzle take?
4. Some natives of Africa talk with drums.
5. Try again, Jeff. Have another go at it.
6. Mary's nails were gleaming.
7. The anchor settled on the sandy bottom.
8. The boys wanted to go skating.
9. Write a letter to a dear friend.

Add-A-Letter Puzzle

From the clues can you guess the words? In each puzzle a short word is repeated four times.

You eat with this.
Twenty plus twenty.
Lots of big trees close together.
To desert or abandon.

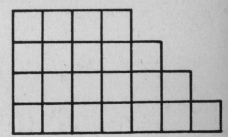

Smooth, shiny cloth.
Planet with rings.
To make content.
Day of the week.

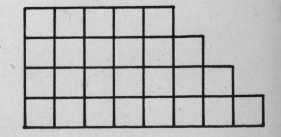

Group of musicians who play together.
Put your money in these.
Long, yellow fruit.
To cover an injury.

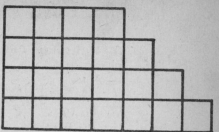

To close one eye.
Fly your kite on _____ days.
Coldest season.
You can look out of these.

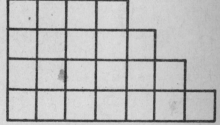

It Makes a Difference

What's the difference between a well-dressed man and a tired dog?

The man wears a suit, the dog just pants.

What's the difference between a crazy rabbit and a counterfeit dollar bill?

One is a mad bunny, and the other is bad money.

What's the difference between a sailor and six broken clocks?

The sailor goes to sea, and the clocks cease to go.

Pig Puzzle Word Find

By going up, down, backward, forward, or diagonally, can you find the words that have to do with pigs and pig stories? Put a loop around each one.

PIG	CORN	WOLF	THREE
SOW	FEED	BRICKS	GRUNT
MUD	BANK	STICKS	WILBUR
HAM	FEET	STRAW	WEB
STY	OINK	SNOUT	

```
        S S
      K B K N A B
    W N E C O W E
      O I W I U A G E
    P L O L R T R S T Y
    I F S O B U T K D O
    G E Y O N U S C U U
    F E E T W T R I M S
    D D E E R H T A
      N R O C A S H
```

Count-Tree Crossword

Across:

1. Tree that rhymes
   with 4 across.
4. To let stand in water.
6. One who uses.
7. Yours in the Bible.
8. Tree fruit for cider.
11. Hickory, pecan, etc.

13. Tree for a partridge.
18. Average (abbrev.).
20. Tree that weeps.
22. Evergreen tree.
23. Third month (abbrev.).
24. Louisiana (abbrev.).
25. Oz Dorothy's Aunt _____ .
27. Minnesota (abbrev.).
28. Fruits of desert palm.

Down:

1. Three _____ puts the other team at bat.
2. The bright-berried mountain
   _____ rhymes with dash.
3. Maple seed or door opener.
4. Juice of trees.
5. Everyone together.
9. Edgar Allen _____ , author of
   great horror stories.
10. Street (abbrev.).
12. United Nations (abbrev.).
13. Tree of tropical islands.
14. Oak fruits for squirrels.
15. Uncooked meat is _____ .
16. Source of pancake syrup.
19. Latin word for "by way of."
20. Dandelion in lawn; grass in garden.
21. A limping horse is _____ .
26. Massachusetts (abbrev.).

Tongue Teaser

Start with the marked T. Moving around the circle three times clockwise, underline every 3rd letter after that T. Keep circling and underlining every 3rd letter until you have made a tongue-twister sentence. This one should tease your tongue for hours!

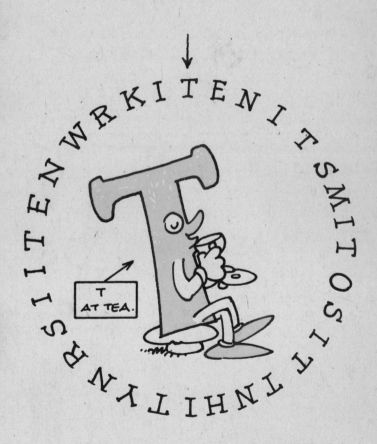

Vanishing Vowels

The vowels (A, E, I, O, U) have disappeared from this story. Put back the vowels and you'll have the whole story.

THE AARDVARK, AN ANIMAL WHICH IS THE FIRST WORD IN THE DICTIONARY, L—V—S —N —FR—C—. H— —S V—RY F—ND —F —NTS. —N F—CT, H— —S C—LL—D —N —NT——T—R. H—'S V—RY G——D —T TH—S J—B, P—RTLY B—C——S— H— B—RR—WS —N TH— GR——ND WH—R— —NTS —FT—N L—V—, —ND P—RTLY B—C——S— H— H—S — L—NG SN——T. W— —R— L—CKY TH—T TH—R— —R— ——RDV—RKS. B—C——S— —F TH—R— W—R—N'T —NY ——RDV—RKS, W— W——LD S——N B— —P T— ——R ——RS —N —NTS! H—RR—H F—R ——RDV—RKS!

What's What?

What holds the sun up in the sky?

Sunbeams.

What causes hives?

Bees.

What do baby apes sleep in?

Apricots.

What is the proper name for shiska-bob?

Shiska-Robert.

Add-Mad Number Find

Put a loop around any *three* numbers that add up to
12 — up, down, backward, forward, or diagonally.

```
6 4 2 6 8 1 3 6 2 5
5 1 5 3 2 9 3 2 8 4
1 4 5 3 2 9 4 7 2 6
2 7 4 1 4 7 5 3 6 2
8 4 5 5 3 3 6 8 4 1
2 6 7 1 4 5 8 5 1 6
5 2 7 6 5 5 2 8 7 5
4 4 4 7 3 2 5 4 3 7
3 8 5 4 3 5 6 4 5 4
6 5 3 1 9 1 2 8 6 1
```

I'M NUMBER ONE!

NO, I'M ONE!

NO, ME!

Across:

1. _____ son, Mississippi.
6. She _____ an egg over his head.
9. Place (abbrev.).
10. Opposite of up.
13. Laurel _____ Hardy.
14. Old Testament (abbrev.).
15. Rail Road (abbrev.).
17. Not hers but _____ .

Down:

2. _____ sent (not present).
3. What a king wears on his head.
4. Knock Out (abbrev.).
5. He tripped and _____ .
7. Kitchen Patrol (abbrev.).
8. Advertisement (abbrev.)
11. A pledge to obey, or a swear word.
12. North Dakota (abbrev.).
16. Rhode Island (abbrev.).

Message from Ma Goose

This *looks* like another crossword. But there's more. When you've filled in all the squares, look for the words in a nursery rhyme. Then write the nursery rhyme under the puzzle.

IS IT "HICKORY DICKORY DOCK"?
IS IT "TOM, TOM, THE PIPER'S SON"?

Happy Holiday Rebus

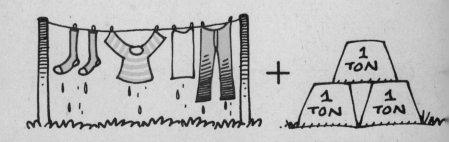

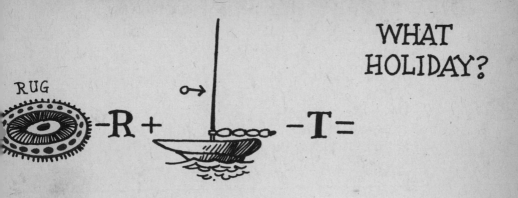

RUG

$-R +$ (boat) $-T =$

$-E +$ (heart) $-$ (hat) $=$

$+$ (lines) $- L + DAY =$

(cake) $- CAKE =$

More Magic Squares

(They'll read the same, up or down.)

N.
1. Opposite of South.
2. Opposite of under, followed by "a":_____ .
3. Name of puzzle like those on pages 34-35.
4. "In God we _____."
5. A hurry; rhymes with paste.

W.
1. Where the sun sets.
2. A girl's name that has a man's nickname in it.
3. To break suddenly with a sharp sound.
4. Strips to bind packages or bandages.

E.
1. Where the sun rises.
2. Word like "oh" with opposite of yes.
3. Stuff that falls in winter.
4. Not a city or village, but a _____.

S.
1. Opposite of North.
2. Fifties rock-and-roll record; a "golden
   _____."
3. Part of a cow that milk comes from.
4. _____ the rope _____ the mast.
5. Big long sandwiches.

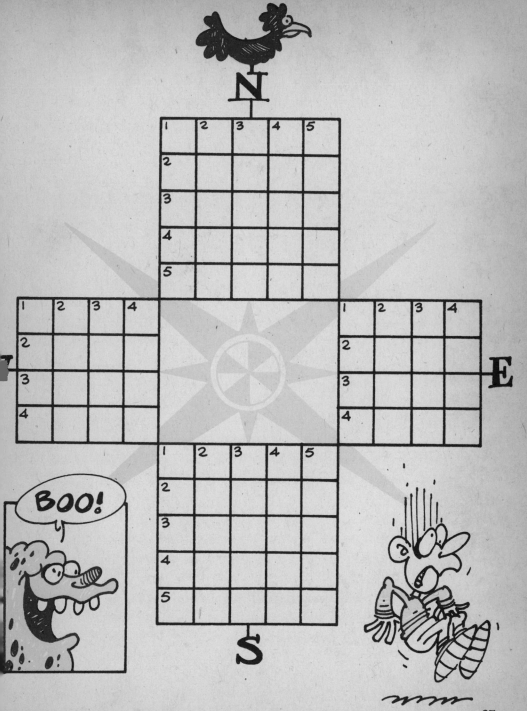

Id Quiz

How many of these famous characters do you know?
Match them by drawing a line from the name to the
creature.

1.	Rudolph	Lion
2.	Flipper	Dog
3.	Bugs	Bear
4.	Morris	Mouse
5.	Elsa	Duck
6.	Smokey	Reindeer
7.	Benji	Dolphin
8.	Charlotte	Cat
9.	Stuart Little	Rabbit
10.	Donald	Horse
11.	Wilbur	Bird
12.	Woodstock	Raccoon
13.	Trigger	Spider
14.	Rascal	Pig

Homonym Hunt

Homonyms are words that sound alike but are spelled differently and have different meanings. In the word find below, can you see the *homonyms* of these words?

BEAR, HAIR, FLOWER, SEE, BY, FUR, BLUE, ANT, TWO, FOUR, WARE, PAIR, SON.

B A R E T R S
A E S R M U U
B U Y A C O N
O T N H I L R
F I R T P F A
O B L E W O E
R A E W R N P
E T M S G R S

WHERE ARE MY **EIGHT** DONUTS?

I ATE 'EM!

Jacks Crossword

Across:

3. This Jack could eat no fat.
5. This fairy tale is called Jack and the _____.
7. All work and no play makes Jack a dull _____.
9. At Halloween, Jack-O-_____ is a popular fellow.
10. _____ Jack is a crunchy treat that most of us like to eat.

Down:

1. This Jack decorates windows in winter.
2. Jack of all _____, master of none, is a well-known old saying.
4. A spring plant is the Jack-in-the-_____.
5. A pop-up toy is a Jack-in-the-_____.
6. This Jack had a plum on his thumb.
8. A short coat.

Monster Mirth

What did Frankenstein say when he ran out of electricity?

"A.C. come, A.C. go."

What monster was in your washing machine?

The wash and wear-wolf.

What is a vampire's favorite holiday?

Fangsgiving

Why does Frankenstein like funny riddles?

Because they keep him in stitches.

What Am I?

You'll find my first letter in STEW,
    but not SET.
My second's in BITE, but it
    isn't BET.
My third is in PLATE, but it's missing
    in PALE.
In CLAIM, find my fourth, but do
    not search in MAIL.
If you're wondering now which
    word this can be,
You'll find the last letter in HEAT,
    but nowhere in TEA.

What am I? __ __ __ __ __

Dog Daze

Help this dazed dog find the bone he buried in the middle of the maze.

H Word Find

Put a loop around the words that start with the letter H in this H-shaped puzzle. You can go up, down, forward, backward, or diagonally.

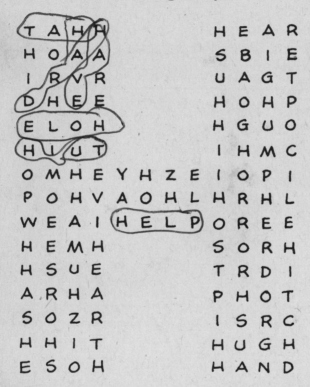

```
T A H H        H E A R
H O A A        S B I E
I R V R        U A G T
D H E E        H O H P
E L O H        H G U O
H I U T        I H M C
O M H E Y H Z E I O P I
P O H V A O H L H R H L
W E A I H E L P O R E E
H E M H        S O R H
H S U E        T R D I
A R H A        P H O T
S O Z R        I S R C
H H I T        H U G H
E S O H        H A N D
```

Word Magic

Make one word into another, changing only one letter at a time.

Turn a tree into a post:

PINE

_____

_____

_____

POST

Turn a seed into a leaf:

SEED

_____

_____

_____

LEAF

Turn grass into a plant:

GRASS

_____

_____

CLANS

_____

PLANT

Camp Trail

Can you find these camp words? Put a loop around each one. You can go up, down, backward, forward, or diagonally.

FIRE, CANTEEN, LANTERN, CAMPING, SLEEPING BAG, KNAPSACK, FLASHLIGHT, TRAILER, TENT, KNIFE, WIENERS, ROPE, MEAT, AXE, PATH, WOODS.

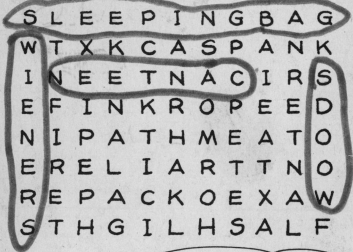

```
S L E E P I N G B A G
W T X K C A S P A N K
I N E E T N A C I R S
E F I N K R O P E E D
N I P A T H M E A T O
E R E L I A R T T N O
R E P A C K O E X A W
S T H G I L H S A L F
```

PORTABLE TELEVISION... COOLER OF SODA POP...FREEZE-DRIED FOOD...I'M ALL SET TO ROUGH IT!

Monster Madness

Start at any letter. Follow its loop to an empty box and write in that letter. When you have moved all the letters to the empty boxes, they will spell the name of a famous movie monster.

Square Dance

In this puzzle, you start with Number 1, and move one square at a time in *any* direction at all, up, down, or sideways, in order to spell out the words for which you have the clues below. Hint: In one way or other, all refer to something black.

¹B	U	T	H	E	P	³B	C
E	A	²S	Y	E	L	A	K
L	⁵B	D	K	C	A	⁴B	B
C	A	R	I	B	L	E	D
K	E	D	S	A	N	A	R
E	Y	U	S	⁶B	A	C	K
T	C	L	⁷B	S	L	E	B
A	K	C	A	E	I	R	R

1. The name of a beautiful horse in a story was Black _____.

2. The name of an animal in a nursery rhyme (Baa Baa Black _____).

3. The name of a cruel, wicked English pirate.

4. In the Mother Goose rhyme, "Sing a Song of Sixpence," what kind of a bird was baked in a pie?

5. This pretty yellow and black centered flower grows along the side of country roads.

6. These little fruits are delicious when baked in tarts.

7. Watch out for this animal on Halloween!

Ding Dong Crossword

Across:

1. Church or dinner _____.
5. What you do with 1 across.
9. Another name for margarine;
   also, O with name for lion.
10. A scent.
11. Exclamation of regret.
12. A prescribed amount of medicine.
13. To record or bind with strips.
14. Past tense of slay.
15. Small vegetables in a pod.
19. Slow sad sound of 1 across; also
    _____ house cookies.
23. A measure of land.
24. Opera song; also, area with i
    instead of e.
25. A poetic way of saying you.
26. Narrow passage through mountains.
27. To let something stand in water.
28. A thin strip of wood.

Down:

1. A small ship.
2. Girl's name; rhymes with umbrella.
3. To jump high.
4. Opposite of win.
5. Lightning or curtain _____ (plural).
6. Statue or person you worship.
7. What we smell with.

8. Past tense of grow.
15. Touches gently.
16. Sound that comes back to you when you shout.
17. Region or cleared space.
18. To look for.
19. Bugle song at night; also gentle knocks.
20. Not a written test, but an _____ (spoken) test.
21. Girl's name (rhymes with visa).
22. Opposite of first.

What Did They Say?

What did the puddle say to the rain?

"Why don't you drop in some time?"

What did the pony say when he coughed?

"Excuse me, I'm just a little hoarse."

What did the river say to the sea?

"It was nice running into you."

What did the mother strawberry say to her children?

"Don't get caught in a jam."

What did the gardener say when he laughed?

"Hoe, hoe, hoe."

Damp Daze

Cross out each odd number. The even-numbered letters that are left will spell out a wet, but well-known saying.

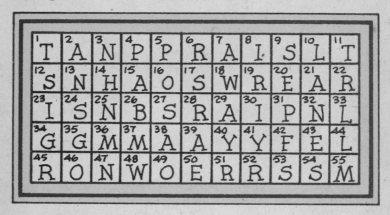

1 T	2 A	3 N	4 P	5 P	6 R	7 A	8 I	9 S	10 L	11 T
12 S	13 N	14 H	15 A	16 O	17 S	18 W	19 R	20 E	21 A	22 R
23 I	24 S	25 N	26 B	27 S	28 R	29 A	30 I	31 P	32 N	33 L
34 G	35 G	36 M	37 M	38 A	39 A	40 Y	41 Y	42 F	43 E	44 L
45 R	46 O	47 N	48 W	49 O	50 E	51 R	52 R	53 S	54 S	55 M

_ _ _ _ _   _ _ _ _ _ _ _

_ _ _ _ _   _ _ _   _ _ _ _ _ _ _

"THE RAIN IN SPAIN FALLS MAINLY ON THE PLAIN"? NO...
"RAIN, RAIN, GO AWAY"? NO...
"IT NEVER RAINS BUT IT POURS"? NO...

T.V. Talk Mix Match

Match up the names of these characters with the job they do on their TV shows.

Hawkeye
    (M*A*S*H)   newscaster

Mary Richards
    (Mary Tyler Moore Show)   window decorater

Fonzie
    (Happy Days)   detective chief

Rhoda   surgeon

Steve Austin
    (Six Million Dollar Man)   bank teller

Kotter
    (Welcome Back, Kotter)   mechanic

Archie Bunker
    (All in the Family)   producer

Barney Miller   teacher

Brenda Morgenstern
    (Rhoda)   dock worker

Laverne and Shirley   super-spy

Ted Baxter
    (Mary Tyler Moore Show)   factory workers

Tongue Twister Acrostic

After finding the right words to fit the definitions, print the letters above the numbers, and write them in the correct squares. You will find they spell a tongue twister.

A. Found inside apples (plural).

$\overline{}\ \overline{}\ \overline{}\ \overline{}\ \overline{}$
7 21 22 25 4

B. What scissors do.

$\overline{}\ \overline{}\ \overline{}$
20 2 13

C. The way out (of an auditorium).

$\overline{}\ \overline{}\ \overline{}\ \overline{}$
3 12 23 27

D. Sound a camera makes.

$\overline{}\ \overline{}\ \overline{}\ \overline{}\ \overline{}$
16 5 19 29 17

E. Frozen water.

$\overline{}\ \overline{}\ \overline{}$
28 24 8

F. Snake sound.

$\overline{}\ \overline{}\ \overline{}\ \overline{}$
14 6 31 10

G. Cover for a pot.

$\overline{}\ \overline{}\ \overline{}$
18 15 9

H. A hug and a _____.

$\overline{}\ \overline{}\ \overline{}\ \overline{}$
30 11 26 1

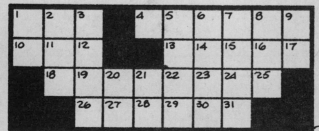

WHAT A TWISTER!

A Touch of the Dutch

Across:
1. Modern name for Holland.
11. To furnish or fit out, as an army.
12. To wait for.
13. To select (rhymes with gull).
15. To enjoy.
16. Back ending of an animal.
17. Past tense of slay.
18. High mountain in Europe (usually plural).
19. One _____ a time.
20. South-South-East (abbrev.).
21. Your mother's brother is your _____.
24. Ocean against which the Dutch have built dikes (2 words).

Down:
1. A sweet juice found in flowers.
2. The same size or amount.
3. Famous flower from Holland.
4. A very small mountain.
5. Epistle (abbrev.).
6. Los Angeles (abbrev.).
7. Pointed tool for punching holes (plural).
8. Hard as _____; also, what carpenters use.
9. The high banks in Holland to keep out the sea.
10. Meat and vegetables simmered together are _____.
14. The Flying _____ man.
19. Small insect.
21. Uranium (abbrev.).
22. Lincoln School (abbrev.).
23. Early English (abbrev.).

Countries Cover-Up

Five countries are cleverly concealed in each of the following 5 sentences. See if you can uncover them.

1. "Let's move the couch in after lunch," said Samantha.

2. "Can a dash of salt really make the stew tastier?" asked Josh.

3. "Mr. Jones says we dented his fender, but we didn't!" protested Tom.

4. "If I could only find a fortune in diamonds," sighed Jenny, wistfully.

5. Said Russ, "I am very thirsty. Please pour me some lemonade."

I THOUGHT DAISY KNITTED THE AFGHAN. I STAND CORRECTED!

NOT HER! SHE'S INTO WOMEN'S LIB, YA KNOW!

I RAN OVER HERE TO TELL YOU THAT!

PUFF

PUFF

Answers

Page 3   *Space Maze*

Page 5   *Name It*
1. pot   2. names (Dan; Will)   3. rope   4. seal   5. star
6. table   7. ring   8. shoe   9. saw   10. leaf

Page 6   *Word Bargain*
1. grounds   2. bark   3. horns   4. eyes   5. ball   6. hands
7. ring   8. slip   9. trip   10. fly

Page 7   *Color Clues*

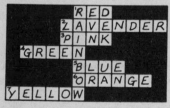

Page 9   *Dates 'n' Stuff*

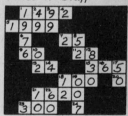

Page 10   *Alphabet Soup*
I;   J;   X;   U;   P;   C;   B;   R;   Q;
B;   C;   T;   G;   O;   Y;   Z;   V

Page 11   *State Scramble:* MINNESOTA

Page 13   *Paint-A-Color*

EASEL

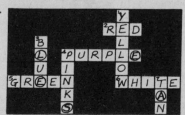

Page 14 *Twist Around:* DO DEER DAILY DREAD DARK DAYS?

Page 15 *Magic Square*

Page 17 *Hidden Saying Rebus:* EARLY TO BED AND
EARLY TO RISE
MAKES A MAN HEALTHY
WEALTHY AND WISE.

Page 19 *Farm Charm Crossword*

Pages 20-21 *Hidden Creature Feature*

1. famous, even   2. do good
3. How long   4. Africa talk
5. go at it.   6. Mary's nails
7. anchor settled
8. boys wanted   9. to a dear

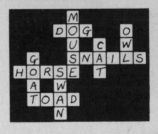

Page 22 *Add-A-Letter Puzzle*

FORK
FORTY
FOREST
FORSAKE

BAND
BANKS
BANANA
BANDAGE

SATIN
SATURN
SATISFY
SATURDAY

WINK
WINDY
WINTER
WINDOWS

Page 25 *Pig Puzzle Word Find*

Page 27 *Count-Tree Crossword*

Page 28 *Tongue Teaser:* TIMOTHY'S TWIN'S TIN
TRINKET IS TINIER

Page 29 *Vanishing Vowels*

THE AARDVARK, AN ANIMAL WHICH IS THE FIRST
WORD IN THE DICTIONARY, LIVES IN AFRICA. HE IS VERY
FOND OF ANTS. IN FACT, HE IS CALLED AN ANTEATER.
HE'S VERY GOOD AT THIS JOB, PARTLY BECAUSE HE
BURROWS IN THE GROUND WHERE ANTS OFTEN LIVE,
AND PARTLY BECAUSE HE HAS A LONG SNOUT. WE ARE
LUCKY THAT THERE ARE AARDVARKS. BECAUSE IF
THERE WEREN'T ANY AARDVARKS, WE WOULD SOON BE
UP TO OUR EARS IN ANTS! HURRAH FOR AARDVARKS!

Page 31 *Add-Mad Number Find*

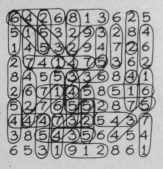

Page 33 *Message From Ma Goose*
JACK FELL DOWN
AND BROKE HIS CROWN

Page 34 *Happy Holiday Rebus*
1. Christmas 2. Easter 3. Valentine's Day
4. Washington's Birthday

Page 37 *More Magic Squares*

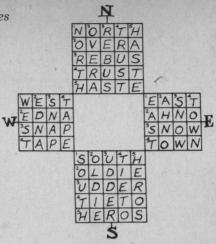

N

N	O	R	T	H
O	V	E	R	A
R	E	B	U	S
T	R	U	S	T
H	A	S	T	E

W	E	S	T
E	D	N	A
S	N	A	P
T	A	P	E

W

E	A	S	T
A	H	N	O
S	N	O	W
T	O	W	N

E

S	O	U	T	H
O	L	D	I	E
U	D	D	E	R
T	I	E	T	O
H	E	R	O	S

S

Page 38 *Id Quiz*

1. reindeer   2. dolphin   3. rabbit   4. cat   5. lion
6. bear   7. dog   8. spider   9. mouse   10. duck   11. pig
12. bird   13. horse   14. raccoon

Page 39 *Homonym Hunt*

Page 41 *Jacks Crossword*

Page 43 *What Am I?* WITCH

Page 44 *Dog Daze*

Page 45 *H Word Find*

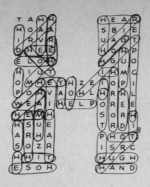

Page 46 *Word Magic*
1. PINE/pint/pant/past/POST
2. SEED/reed/read/lead/LEAF
3. GRASS/glass/class/CLANS/plans/PLANT

Page 47 *Camp Trail*

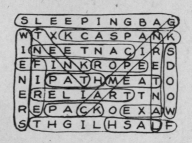

Page 48 *Monster Madness:* KING KONG

Page 49 *Square Dance*
1. Beauty   2. Sheep
3. Blackbeard   4. blackbird   5. black-eyed Susan
6. blackberries   7. black cat.

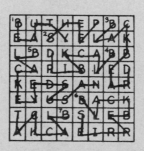

Page 51   *Ding Dong Crossword*

¹B	²E	³L	⁴L		⁵R	⁶I	⁷N	⁸G

Grid 1:
¹B	²E	³L	⁴L	⁵R	⁶I	⁷N	⁸G
⁹O	L	E	O	¹⁰O	D	O	R
¹¹A	L	A	S	¹²D	O	S	E
¹³T	A	P	E	¹⁴S	L	E	W

Grid 2:
¹⁵P	¹⁶E	¹⁷A	¹⁸S	¹⁹T	²⁰O	²¹L	²²L
²³A	C	R	E	²⁴A	R	I	A
²⁵T	H	E	E	²⁶P	A	S	S
²⁷S	O	A	K	²⁸S	L	A	T

Page 53   *Damp Daze:* APRIL SHOWERS BRING MAY
FLOWERS

Page 54   *T.V. Talk Mix Match*
Hawkeye, surgeon; Mary Richards, producer; Fonzie, mechanic;
Rhoda, window decorator; Steve Austin, super-spy; Kotter,
teacher; Archie Bunker, dock worker; Barney Miller, detective
chief; Brenda Morgenstern, bank teller; Laverne and Shirley,
factory workers; Ted Baxter, newscaster.

Page 55   *Tongue Twister Acrostic*
A. CORES   B. CUT   C. EXIT
D. CLICK   E. ICE   F. HISS
G. LID   H. KISS

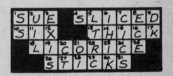

Page 57   *A Touch of the Dutch*

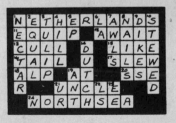

Page 58   *Countries Cover-Up*
1. couch in after   2. Can a dash
3. says we dented
4. fortune in diamonds   5. Russ. I am